Abnormal Psychology

EPHRAIM ROSEN

LATE PROFESSOR OF PSYCHOLOGY
UNIVERSITY OF MINNESOTA

IAN GREGORY

ASSOCIATE PROFESSOR OF PSYCHIATRY
UNIVERSITY OF MINNESOTA

W. B. SAUNDERS COMPANY

PHILADELPHIA AND LONDON

Reprinted March, 1966, September, 1967 and
April, 1968

Abnormal Psychology

It is a thing of no great difficulty to raise objections
against another man's oration — nay, it is a very easy
matter; but to produce a better in its place is a work
extremely troublesome.

Plutarch, *Of Hearing*

PREFACE

Any comprehensive view of man's behavior must be based on information from a variety of disciplines that include genetics, physiology, biochemistry, psychology, sociology and anthropology. Because of the tremendous advances being made in each field of study, however, scholars have tended to become isolated by specialization. Even in such closely related disciplines as psychology, psychoanalysis and psychiatry, students are frequently unaware of each other's literature and viewpoints, and may therefore be unable to communicate effectively. This is not the first textbook of abnormal psychology to be written jointly by a psychologist and a psychiatrist, but we believe it is unique in its attempt to integrate psychoanalytic theory, experimental psychology and practical clinical experience with research in the various biological and social sciences.

This book is divided into two parts, the first an introduction to the general principles of abnormal psychology, and the second an application of these principles to the analysis of each of the main syndromes of abnormal behavior. Part One, and each chapter in Part Two, are structured in terms of definition and description, development and dynamics, causation and treatment. This

method of analyzing abnormal behavior has provided a logical basis for the presentation of the subject matter as a whole. Within this systematic framework we are concerned with such questions as: What is abnormality? What abnormal behavior is associated with a given diagnosis? What are the characteristic dynamics or modes of adaptation? What is the developmental history? What causal factors probably initiated or perpetuated this abnormal behavior? What approaches to treatment have been adopted?

The desire to simplify information for the undergraduate student sometimes leads to a glossing over of conflicting findings or interpretations, and the presentation of a one-sided or reductionistic point of view. This book, however, is intended for serious students, and there has been no attempt to avoid any aspect of the subject because of difficulty or controversy. We have not avoided discussion of methodological issues, presentation of contradictory evidence, or use of statistics and tables. We have taken great pains, however, to explain every new concept clearly and to use whatever forms of illustration seemed desirable for clarification, including a large number of case histories which are discussed in some detail. The latter are not restricted to any particular age group or socioeconomic status, but include a representative selection of cases seen in private offices, public clinics, general hospitals and various institutions restricted to psychiatric patients.

This was a collaboration that grew closer as we moved from the discussion of general principles in Part One to the systematic analysis of specific syndromes in Part Two. Unfortunately, Professor Rosen died suddenly before the manuscript was completed. I shared a deep sense of loss with his family, colleagues and students, but I am most grateful for the assistance of his wife, Sylvia W. Rosen, in completing the work, and of Shirley H. Mink, Ph.D., who worked with me in writing Chapters 21 and 22.

I wish to express my sincere appreciation to Rose Boucher and Marie Hart for their invaluable secretarial services. I am also indebted to the various authors and publishers who kindly consented to our reproducing tables, figures and other materials, which receive individual acknowledgment in the text.

IAN GREGORY

CONTENTS

CONTENTS

PART TWO   SPECIFIC SYNDROMES

PART ONE

General
Principles

Mental disease appears greatly to tax the attention of good observers because it presents itself to us as a mixture of incoherence and confusion.

Philippe Pinel, Introduction to *Medical-Philosophic Treatise on Mania*, 1801

INTRODUCTION: THE NATURE AND SCOPE OF ABNORMAL PSYCHOLOGY

For thousands of years men have observed their environment and themselves and have sought to explain their observations. One set of phenomena—nightmares, unusual and incomprehensible speech, convulsive fits, violent emotional responses and other dramatic departures from routine behavior—long ago came to be regarded as especially intriguing and in need of explanation. Meanwhile, ordinary behavior also claimed man's attention. In the nineteenth century, after millennia of uncontrolled observation and speculation, mental processes and behavior began to be studied under laboratory conditions, and the science of general psychology was established. Within a few years, initial attempts were made to relate the methods of general psychology to behavior deviations, and modern abnormal psychology was born.

Abnormal psychology is the application of the methods, concepts, principles and findings of general psychology—primarily, the psychology of perception, learning and development, and social psychology—to deviant behaviors and experiences. Abnormal psychology is an attempt to understand and explain the abnormal in the framework of the normal and general. This definition is incomplete, however, for it does not specify what is meant by "abnormal" or "deviant." The criteria for judging that a behavior or experience is abnormal are discussed later in the chapter.

In this chapter the nature of abnormal psychology is explored as follows: First, some examples of abnormal behaviors and experiences are described and analyzed. Immediately following, the question of how and why such phenomena are judged abnormal is discussed. The next section illustrates the usefulness and also the difficulties of applying the concepts of general psychology to abnormal behavior. Since biology and sociology, as well as general psychology, are rich sources for the understanding of abnormal phenomena, the following two sections illustrate the application of biological and sociocultural concepts to abnormal behavior. The discussion then focuses on a philosophical problem posed by the fact that abnormal psychology is concerned with both psychological and biological phenomena. This is the classic problem of the relation of mind to body. Last, the major topics of abnormal psychology are listed.

EXAMPLES OF DEVIANT BEHAVIOR AND EXPERIENCE

Let us look at three examples as an introduction to the data and concepts of abnormal psychology.

CASE 1. A 35-year-old man had been working as a salesman for a large corporation for several years. His progress was satisfactory to his company, his family and himself. He was promoted to the position of sales manager and began his new work with great optimism, confidence and eagerness. He received excellent cooperation from his associates. But within a couple of months it became clear that something was wrong. He had always been accurate in numerical computation but now he began to make errors. He sometimes addressed people in an offensive manner. He began to sleep badly, smiled much less than formerly and often seemed irritable, upset and depressed. Occasionally he expressed the feeling that he could not handle the job and that he must be stupid or incompetent. Then he decided that his only problem was that some of his colleagues were against him and were sabotaging him. In previous years he drank liquor on social occasions only, but now he began to drink more often, frequently when alone.

ANALYSIS. Our definition of abnormal psychology referred to the two realms of behavior and experience. Abnormalities of both are present in the unhappy sales manager. A number of his difficulties are purely behavioral and can be observed objectively, and some can even be quantified numerically. His increasing inefficiency, difficulty in sleeping (insomnia), change in facial expression, increased frequency of aggressive language and increased consumption of alcohol are all observable phenomena. But his feelings of depression, wavering self-confidence and belief that others were undermining him are not directly observable; they are subjective experiences that have to be inferred from behavior. An important part of abnormal psychology is concerned with such experiences. A disturbed individual's self-concept, feelings of inferiority, unexpressed hostility and guilt feelings are as important as his overt speech and motor behavior. For the sake of convenience, however, the term "behavior" is often used to stand for both behavior and experience.

The sales manager's difficulties also illustrate the fact that deviant phenomena vary in seriousness and degree of irrationality. His unfounded conviction that he was being persecuted constitutes a delusion. Most people would agree that a delusion is more serious than such difficulties as insomnia or irritability. Each of these is a *symptom*, that is, a manifestation of an illness or emotional disturbance.

Symptoms almost never come singly but occur in clusters called *syndromes*. For example, one of the syndromes of psychological disturbance, involutional melancholia, includes such symptoms as feelings of guilt, agitated restlessness, anxiety and fears, delusional ideas and suicidal impulses. Another syndrome, compulsive personality, consists of symptoms that exaggerate common personality traits, particularly excessive orderliness, obstinacy and stinginess. A given syndrome is more severe in some cases than in others; there are mild and severe compulsives, and mild and severe melancholics.

Symptoms may be grouped into several categories. The sales manager's numerical errors and delusion of persecution are deviations of intelligence and thought. His depression is a deviation of affect, mood or feeling. His anxiety, increased use of alcohol, aggressiveness and loss of confidence indicate disordered motivation. Two other categories of symptoms are frequent: symptoms of disordered sensation and perception, and of verbal and motor behavior. These will all be encountered in later discussions of the different syndromes.

CASE 2. A staff sergeant in World War II adjusted well to noncombat duties during the first two years of his army service. In his third year he was in combat for months on end and developed symptoms in one leg that appeared to be due to sciatica. (Sciatica is pain in those regions of the thigh and leg that are innervated by the sciatic nerve.) He began to have nightmares in which he tried to escape from pursuing monsters. During the day, he manifested a number of physiological signs of anxiety: excessive sweating, shaking, muscular weakness and facial pallor. The sciatic symptoms soon disappeared, but he became completely paralyzed in both legs. Medical examination revealed no physical basis for this symptom and it was concluded that its origin was emotional. He was discharged from the armed services and in time the paralysis vanished almost completely. However, new behavior difficulties soon appeared. He began to beat his wife and children brutally and to get into fist fights with casual acquaintances. He was jailed three times and fired from 15 successive jobs. Finally, when he experienced a strong impulse to "punch a bus in the nose," he realized that he needed help and voluntarily committed himself to a hospital.

ANALYSIS. To understand this case it is necessary to explore the complex concept of *anxiety*. The patient manifested anxious *responses* such as sweating and shaking. Anxiety is a *drive* as well as a type of response; it motivated much of the patient's behavior. For example, his leg paralysis was an unconscious, involuntary, defensive attempt to avoid being overwhelmed by anxious feelings. So long as he could not move he could not be sent into combat. On a conscious level he did not fear combat at all and in fact rather gloried in it, but in order to understand his behavior we must assume that he was unconsciously afraid. His nightmares support the assumption for they are indicative of anxiety. The case thus illustrates the fact that explanations of abnormal phenomena involve unconscious as well as conscious processes.

Although the paralysis was ameliorated when he was discharged from the army, the patient's unconscious anxiety then drove him to aggressive behavior toward his family, comparative strangers and even inanimate objects. Combat fear was gone but his anxiety had become chronic. *Anxiety is evidenced in so many ways, is an important component of so many disorders, and can persist for so long a time that it may be considered the central concept of modern abnormal psychology.*

CASE 3. A 55-year-old woman with no prior history of difficulties began to deteriorate mentally. Fairly simple intellectual problems became impossible for her to solve, particularly if they involved abstract ideas or generalizations. She became disoriented: she did not know where she was, the month of the year or the identity of people with whom she had talked many times. Her memory became vague, especially for recent events. Frequently she would make silly, pointless statements and repeat meaningless phrases over and over. She liked being with people and was interested in the happenings around her, yet her emotional responses lacked richness, variation and subtlety to the extent that she seemed childlike. In time her speech became incoherent and she developed such muscular difficulties as partial paralyses and convulsions.

ANALYSIS. Behavior of this sort is characteristic of patients with a severe brain disorder. The case just cited is an example of *Alzheimer's disease*, a progressive, widespread deterioration of the cerebral cortex that severely impairs intellectual functioning.

In the first two cases no medical factors operated causally (except for an attack of sciatica preceding the sergeant's leg paralysis). In the present case the patient's symptoms can be understood only as a consequence of medical causes. Psychological abnormality may result from emotional, nonmedical, so-called "functional" causes; medical, so-called "organic" causes; or both.

WHAT IS ABNORMALITY?

The cases cited demonstrate that abnormality embraces many different and complicated phenomena. These may be objective or subjective; may be relatively severe or mild; and may occur as difficulties of intellectual functioning, affect and mood, motivation, perception and motor and verbal behavior. The phenomena of abnormality often require analysis at both conscious and unconscious levels. Finally, they may or may not involve organic difficulties. The diversity and complexity of the phenomena of abnormality are so great that it is no easy matter to formulate an all-inclusive definition of the term "abnormal."

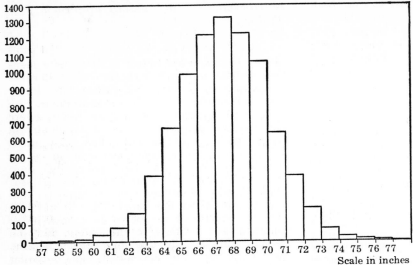

Figure 1–1. Histogram for heights of 8585 men. (From Holzinger, K. J. 1928. Statistical Methods for Students in Education. Boston, Ginn and Co.)

Psychologists and psychiatrists have suggested several different criteria to discriminate the normal from the abnormal. The three most frequently suggested are the *statistical* criterion, the criterion of *personal discomfort* and the criterion of *social nonconformity*. Each one is useful, but each also has serious shortcomings.

Abnormality Defined Statistically

The starting point for the statistical criterion is the fact that many traits of subhuman and human organisms are measurable and can be ordered into a frequency distribution. Physical traits such as height, weight, leg length, finger length, head diameter and chest girth, to list but a few, can be measured quite accurately. The distribution of such measurements often has the familiar bell shape of the normal curve.

Some decades ago investigators began to approach psychological traits in this fashion, and now measuring scales exist for many traits. Often the scales have been so constructed that the distributions are close to normal. To mention a few diverse examples, we can measure the intelligence of children and adults, the number of aggressive acts nursery-school children display toward playmates and the emotionality of white rats (as indicated by frequency of defecation and urination).

The only prerequisites for a statistical definition of abnormality in a given trait are the selection of two points on the trait distribution and the stipulation that scores between these cutting points be termed normal and those outside the points be termed abnormal. For instance, we can select the 10th and 90th percentiles in a distribution. Emotionality in the rat, aggressive acts, suicidal impulses, difficulty in sleeping, alcoholic consumption or any other trait or behavior may then be termed abnormal when its intensity or frequency falls below the 10th percentile of the population or above the 90th. The abnormal may thus be equated with a strictly quan-

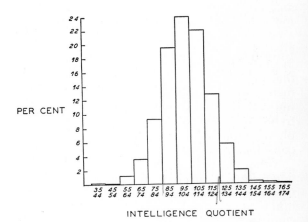

INTELLIGENCE QUOTIENT

Figure 1–2. The distribution of intelligence quotients in the United States. (Modified from Measuring Intelligence, by Drs. L. M. Terman and M. A. Merrill. Reprinted from Human Heredity by J. V. Neel and W. J. Schull by permission of The University of Chicago Press. Copyright 1954 by The University of Chicago.)

titative departure from the typical or average.

The statistical criterion of abnormality has a strong appeal for the psychologist who is eager to put abnormal psychology on a firmly scientific basis. But a rigid application of the criterion involves us in several difficulties.

The Problem of Arbitrary Divisions. The placement of the cutting points that divide a frequency distribution into normal and abnormal regions is arbitrary. An I.Q. of 80 will be termed abnormal if 90 is chosen as a cutting point but not if 70 is chosen. Furthermore, people do not fall into the two simple classes of bright and dull; they are *more or less* bright (or dull).

The same consideration holds for any other trait so that there is no justification for the selection of any point whatsoever to effect a rigid division of behavior or subjective experience into the two classes of normal and abnormal. Analysis of the statistical criterion of abnormality thus leads to the important conclusion that there is a gradual continuum from the normal to the abnormal instead of a sharp separation between the two. The abnormal is usually an exaggeration of the normal.

The concept of a normal-abnormal continuum has two desirable consequences. First, it provides a logical basis for the generalization to abnormal phenomena of principles drawn from studies of normal individuals, as called for by our definition of abnormal psychology. Second, the idea of a normal-abnormal continuum leads to attitudes of sympathy and acceptance toward the emotionally disturbed and mentally ill. The realization that a patient has much in common with us, no matter how disorganized and irrational his behavior may seem at first blush, may motivate efforts to understand and help him. One sees something of the patient in oneself and something of oneself in the patient.

The Problem of Combining Scores. Sometimes it is desirable to characterize as more or less deviant an entire syndrome or even a person, rather than a single trait or behavior. To do this statistically it is necessary to combine several measures into a total score. Suppose, for example, that an individual is troubled by hallucinations, physiological signs of anxiety and gaps in memory. Suppose further—hypothetical as this supposition may be—that each of these symptoms could be expressed as a score. If we tried to combine the three scores we would not know how much weight to give each, for we do not know the relative importance of each symptom in every syndrome. Weighting symptoms equally would ignore the fact that they vary in importance. Since the typical syndrome includes far more than three symptoms, it becomes quite impossible to derive a meaningful abnormality score for a syndrome or a person.

The Problem of Different Dimensions. The problem of weighting symptoms is complicated by the fact that there may be more than one fundamental way of being abnormal. The distinction between *neurosis* and *psychosis* illustrates this point. In neurotic disturbances, the individual suffers from internal conflicts, anxiety and an inability to integrate his drives with his moral standards and inhibitions. He attempts to defend himself against anxiety and fails, but he is rational and he perceives the outer world fairly accurately. The psychotic individual, on the other hand, either because of brain malfunctioning or emotional conflict, tends to misinterpret reality, may fail to communicate meaningfully with other people and is often lost in disorganized and irrational thought processes. A popular joke embodies the difference between the two: the psychotic thinks two and two make five; the neurotic knows perfectly well that two and two make four but it makes him nervous.

The implication of this distinction between neurosis and psychosis is that the dimension or continuum of normal-neurotic may be quite different from the dimension of normal-psychotic. There may be two independent axes of abnormality. In general, we tend to think of psychosis as more severe than neurosis because of the psychotic's defective relation to reality, yet we cannot say that a psychotic is *merely* more abnormal than a neurotic. Psychosis is not neurosis-plus. Although a neurotic patient sometimes becomes psychotic at a later time, more often he remains neurotic. Similarly, the psychotic seldom changes into a neurotic. Furthermore, there are relatively mild psychotics and relatively severe neurotics.

An additional modification of the statistical criterion of abnormality thus becomes necessary: we must substitute the plural "statistical criteria" for the singular "statistical criterion." In fact, the two continua of normal-neurotic and normal-psychotic are almost certainly not enough; a complete map of psychological abnormality would require still other dimensions.

The Problem of Inequality of Extremes. One more difficulty is our reluctance to term both extremes of a distribution abnormal unless somehow we can distinguish between them. Statistically, the genius is as abnormal as the mentally retarded individual; almost complete freedom from conflicts is as abnormal as being ridden by conflicts; and an extremely accurate perception of reality is as rare and abnormal as a marked distortion of reality. But there is a world of difference between the abnormally disturbed and the abnormally supernormal or between the dullard and the genius: one end of the continuum is considered undesirable and the other desirable. Strictly statistical criteria cannot by themselves dictate judgments of desirability and undesirability. They must be supplemented by nonstatistical considerations if we are to be consistent with the universal assumption that health is better than sickness.

Abnormality Defined as Personal Discomfort

A second approach defines abnormality as the degree of discomfort felt by the individual. If he is depressed, unhappy, upset or troubled by inability to control his thoughts he is abnormal. If he is relatively untroubled and indifferent to his inner state and to the impression he makes on others, or if he manifests a state of well-being and euphoria, he is normal no matter how deviant his behavior appears to observers.

It should be noted that this approach is implicitly statistical, for it assumes that people can be described as more or less uncomfortable. However, personal discomfort refers to only one kind of variable whereas the completely statistical criterion proposes to scale all behaviors and experiences. There are difficulties in the personal discomfort criterion, too. These stem from the fact that a disturbed person's complaints, moods, feelings and fears, although important, are an incomplete part of the picture.

The Problem of Subjective vs. Objective Symptoms. The discomfort criterion omits all consideration of behavior deviations that are not accompanied by subjective distress. A patient in the manic phase of the psychotic disorder termed manic-depressive reaction is likely to report that he feels fine, that his daily life is full of things that interest him and that he is sitting on top of the world. Yet he cannot be considered normal for he does not function efficiently in intellectual tasks, he is physically overactive, his speech may be hard to follow and he may hear nonexistent voices. These objective signs cannot be ignored; his euphoric condition is itself a symptom of his manic condition.

The Problem of the Individual's Reaction to His Discomforts. The discomfort criterion omits the important matter of how an individual adjusts to his own feeling states. Two equally depressed persons, for example, may behave very differently: one resists his depressive feelings and struggles to carry on his daily activities and the other submits as if it were futile to expend energy on any activity whatever. Most of us would regard the second individual as far more ill than the first. A criterion of abnormality that does not distinguish between such diametrically different adjustments to felt discomfort is inadequate.

The Problem of Social Consequences. A final inadequacy of the discomfort criterion is its failure to consider the effect of deviant behavior on other people. To return to the thumbnail description of mania, it can be seen that a drop in intellectual efficiency may create difficulties for one's coworkers; confused speech puzzles and may upset people; and physical overactivity in a few cases leads to assaultive behavior. So important, in fact, are the social aspects of abnormality that it has been suggested that they alone are sufficient to define abnormality.

Abnormality Defined as Social Nonconformity

From birth on, the individual lives in a social framework. Society expects him to conform to its standards with certain permitted exceptions. He is rewarded if he conforms and punished if he does not. The criterion of social nonconformity emerges from these considerations: an individual is deemed abnormal to the degree that he fails to conform to social standards and expectations.

Basically, this criterion is also statistical since it defines degree of abnormality by degree of nonconformity. The criterion has five major difficulties.

The Problem of Criminality. It is important to distinguish crime from psychological abnormality. Many criminals are disturbed psychologically—they are particularly likely to belong to a category known as sociopathic personality—but some criminals are psychologically normal despite the fact that they are nonconformists. Crime is a legal, not a psychological, concept. The criminal violates the legal code of society; most disturbed individuals do not violate it or else violate it only as a secondary consequence of psychological disturbance (for example, bodily assault due to delusions). If a careful distinction is not made between criminal and psychological nonconformity there is a danger of incorrectly labeling all criminals as mentally ill, or—even worse—of labeling all mentally ill persons as criminals and thus countering the humanitarian attitude toward mental illness.

The Problem of Cultural Relativity. What constitutes conformity in one culture may constitute nonconformity in another. A few examples drawn from the field of cultural anthropology will illustrate the point.

If a member of a New Guinea tribe, the Kwoma, is frustrated by anyone but a relative he is expected to respond with strong verbal and physical aggression, even to the point of killing the individual who has frustrated him. Such behavior is unacceptable in our culture.

Among the Hopi Indians of the Southwest, on the other hand, both competitiveness and aggression are suppressed to a degree that would seem abnormal to most of us. Hopis show so strong a reluctance to outshine or disapprove of others that in our culture their behavior would undoubtedly be labeled, "abnormally passive"; conversely, our tendency to compete in work and play and to respond aggressively when we feel threatened would constitute social nonconformity in Hopi society. The Hopis also display an intense fear of supernatural forces that would be labeled "anxiety reaction" in our culture.

One need not go outside our own culture to demonstrate variation in cultural expectancies and behavior. Within a single complex culture there are different subcultures: for example, it has been shown repeatedly that members of different classes in our culture respond differently in their thinking, emotional reactions and speech. One consequence of this diversity is that psychiatric diagnoses depend in part on the background and class-conditioned values of the diagnostician. If he shares upper or middle-class values, the speech and thinking patterns of a lower-class patient may appear strange to him and he may be readier to diagnose such a patient as psychotic than one from his own class whose patterns of speech and thought are familiar.

Many writers in abnormal psychology have hoped to find an absolute criterion of abnormality that would be independent of time, place and cultural context. Since abnormality is relative to a particular cultural background, the social nonconformity criterion cannot be absolute.

The Problem of Undesirable Social Standards. A danger of the nonconformity criterion is that it may lead to the assumption that society is always right and the nonconforming individual always at fault. This assumption ignores the fact that cultures vary in their adequacy; cultural change is sometimes more desirable than conformity. The social nonconformity criterion of abnormality has at times been misused to argue for blind conformity to an undesirable status quo.

The Problem of the Cultural Innovator. Related to the preceding problem is the danger of ignoring the fact that progress in human affairs has almost always been brought about by the efforts of innovators who took new paths in art, science and other domains. It is a mistake to assume that every nonconformist is a genius, but it is equally fallacious to assume that all innovators are merely abnormal.

The Problem of the Conforming Neurotic. Most neurotics conform to social expectations more closely than do psychotics, so that the nonconformity criterion is not as readily applicable to neurosis as to psychosis. In fact, some neurotics are marked by a rigid overconformity.

Society maintains jails for the criminally nonconforming and hospitals for the psychiatrically nonconforming. Because of their nonconformity, psychotics are hospitalized far more often than neurotics; the criterion of social nonconformity, despite all its problems and difficulties, is usually the actual basis of a family, medical or legal decision to hospitalize a disturbed individual. The outwardly conforming, unhappy neurotic constitutes a fairly small percentage of involuntarily hospitalized patients. (However, there is an increasing trend for disturbed persons to hospitalize themselves voluntarily, and many such patients are neurotic rather than psychotic.)

Other Approaches to the Definition of Abnormality

In addition to the three fundamental criteria just explored, several others have been proposed, particularly for distinguishing mental illness (psychosis), rather than neurosis, from mental health. An excellent discussion by William A. Scott in Sarbin's *Studies in Behavior Pathology* (1961) describes the following approaches:

Mental Illness Defined as Exposure to Psychiatric Treatment. This definition, commonly used in research on the mentally ill, states simply that anyone who has been treated for a mental disorder, especially in a hospital, can be categorized as mentally ill and everyone else as mentally healthy.

There are two major limitations to this approach. Since diagnostic errors occur, not everyone who has been hospitalized for mental illness can be presumed to have been mentally ill. Second, despite their nonconforming behavior, many mentally ill persons have never been identified as such. A study by Roth and Luton (1943) indicated that the number of psychotics in the community who had not been hospitalized was almost equal to the number who had.

Mental Illness Defined as Maladjustment. The maladjustment criterion may be viewed as a special form of the social nonconformity criterion. It uses some one index of nonconformity, such as community opinion of an individual or suicidal attempts, as the touchstone of maladjustment. The limitations of such an index are identical with the limitations of the nonconformity criterion already discussed, plus two additional difficulties. First, the choice of a specific index is unavoidably arbitrary. Second, different indices may not classify individuals the same way; for example, a suicidal individual may stand high in community opinion.

Mental Illness Defined by Objective Assessment of Psychological Symptoms. In this approach, personality tests are used to measure illness and health. An example is the Minnesota Multiphasic Personality Inventory (MMPI). This test defines abnormality on an objective basis by comparing an individual's test answers with those made by normals and by specified psychiatric groups, such as depressives, manics and schizophrenics. The test yields scores for degree of depression, degree of mania, and so forth. But the problem of combining scores for different dimensions arises since they cannot be easily combined into an overall estimate of abnormality. More important, all present-day tests are subject to errors of unreliability and invalidity; assessment of mental illness on the basis of tests alone, with no attention paid to such factors as past history, is risky. It is possible that future improvements in psychological testing will make such limitations less serious.

Mental Health Defined as Positive Striving. This criterion reverses the usual procedure and attempts to define mental health rather than mental illness. It asserts that healthy people strive to live up to their potentialities and to develop toward greater psychological maturity, and are able to cope with stress. Illness means inability to do these things.

The criterion often clashes with both the nonconformity and the personal discomfort criteria, because the individual who strives and achieves need not be a conformist and may often be tense and uncomfortable. Another limitation is that the choice of behaviors defining health reflects ethical values. Defining health as positive striving is equivalent to the ethical judgment that people *ought* to strive. Very different